TAKE THAT *Beautifu*

© 2007 by International Music Publications Ltd
First published by International Music Publications Ltd in 2007
International Music Publications Ltd is a Faber Music company
3 Queen Square, London WC1N 3AU

Arranged & Engraved by Camden Music
Edited by Lucy Holliday

Photograph from Redferns Music Library

Printed in England by Caligraving Ltd

The text paper used in this publication is a virgin fibre product that is manufactured in the UK
to ISO 14001 standards. The wood fibre used is only sourced from managed forests using
sustainable forestry principles. This paper is 100% recyclable

ISBN10: 0-571-52886-4
EAN13: 978-0-571-52886-8

To buy Faber Music publications or to find out about the full range of titles available,
please contact your local music retailer or Faber Music sales enquiries:

Faber Music Ltd, Burnt Mill, Elizabeth Way, Harlow, CM20 2HX England
Tel: +44(0)1279 82 89 82 Fax: +44(0)1279 82 89 83
sales@fabermusic.com fabermusic.com

Reach Out: 5

Patience: 10

Beautiful World: 16

Hold On: 23

Like I Never Loved You At All: 30

Shine: 36

I'd Wait For Life: 42

Ain't No Sense In Love: 47

What You Believe In: 54

Mancunian Way: 61

Wooden Boat: 67

Butterfly: 72

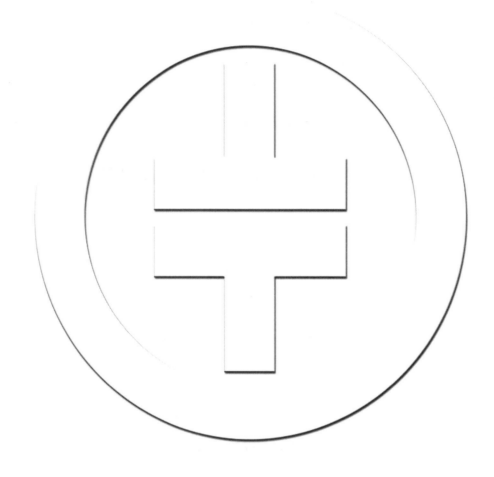

REACH OUT

Words and Music by Gary Barlow, Jason Orange,
Howard Donald, Mark Owen and John Shanks

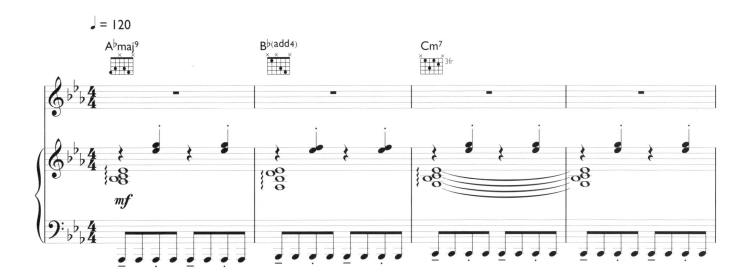

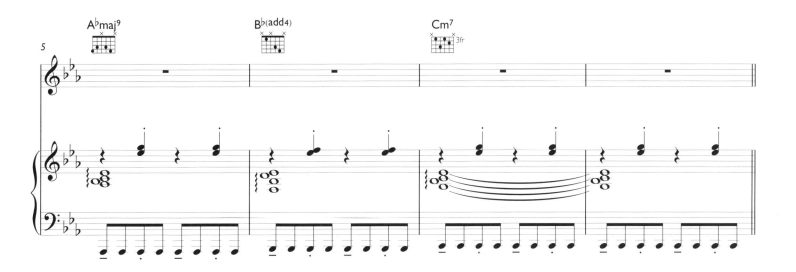

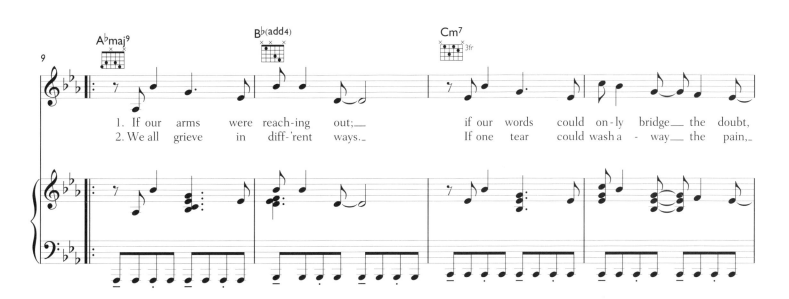

1. If our arms were reach-ing out;___ if our words could on-ly bridge___ the doubt,
2. We all grieve in diff-'rent ways.___ If one tear could wash a - way___ the pain,___

PATIENCE

Words and Music by Gary Barlow, Jason Orange,
Howard Donald, Mark Owen and John Shanks

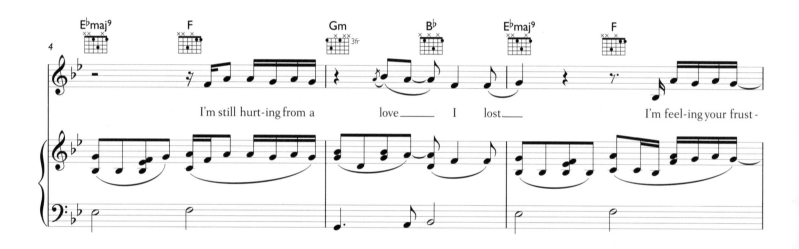

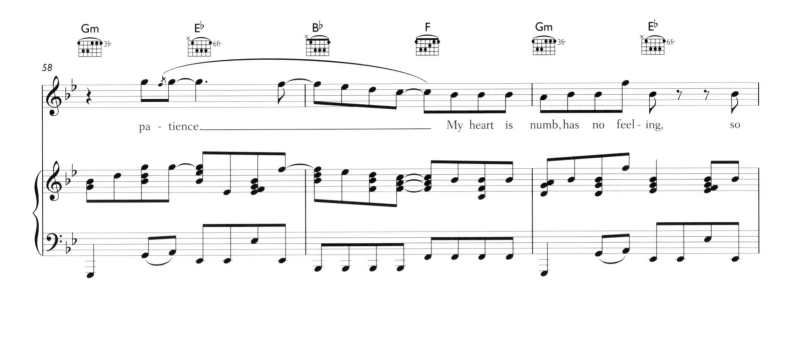

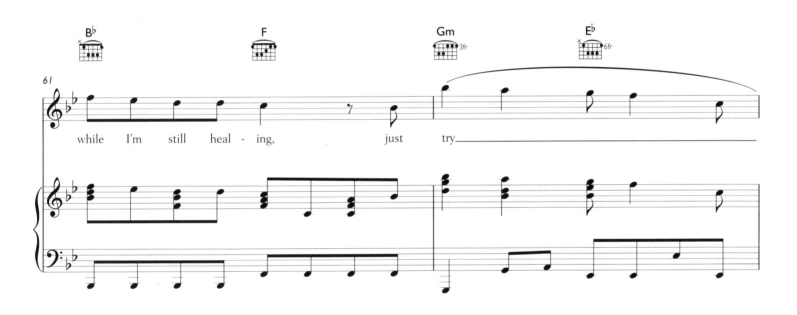

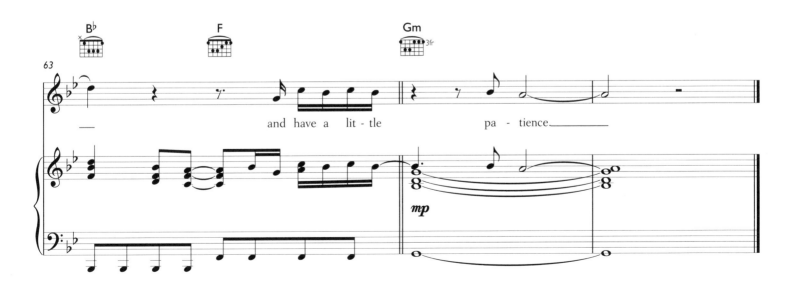

BEAUTIFUL WORLD

Words and Music by Gary Barlow, Jason Orange,
Howard Donald, Mark Owen and Steve Robson

HOLD ON

Words and Music by Gary Barlow, Jason Orange,
Howard Donald, Mark Owen and John Shanks

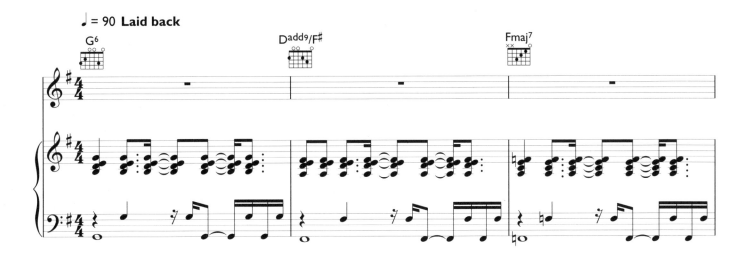

We've been here ma-ny times be-fore,

leav-ing rooms and slam-ming doors,   we're climb-ing up   the bed-room walls,

LIKE I NEVER LOVED YOU AT ALL

Words and Music by Gary Barlow, Jason Orange,
Howard Donald, Mark Owen and John Shanks

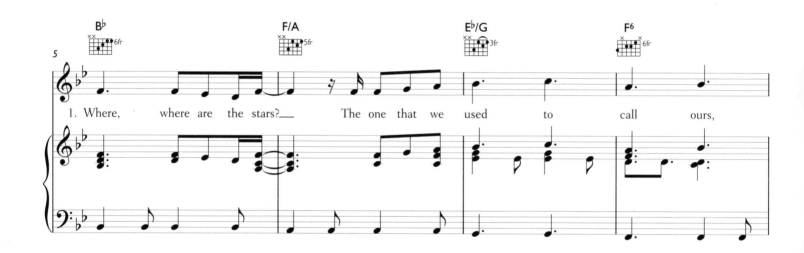

SHINE

Words and Music by Gary Barlow, Jason Orange,
Howard Donald, Mark Owen and Steve Robson

I'D WAIT FOR LIFE

Words and Music by Gary Barlow, Jason Orange,
Howard Donald and Mark Owen

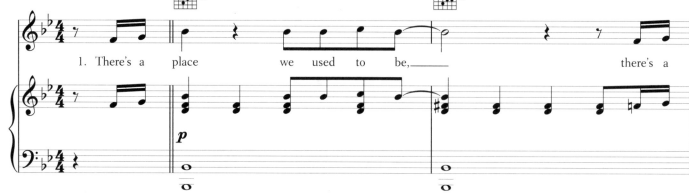

1. There's a place we used to be,_____ there's a

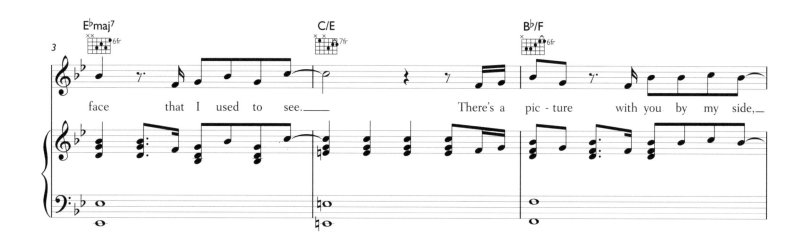

face that I used to see.____ There's a pic- ture with you by my side,_

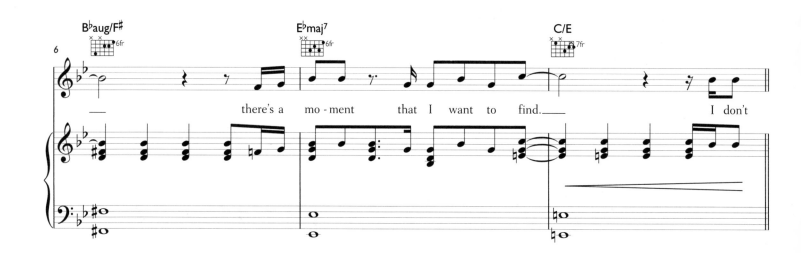

there's a mo- ment that I want to find.____ I don't

AIN'T NO SENSE IN LOVE

Words and Music by Gary Barlow, Jason Orange,
Howard Donald, Mark Owen and Billy Mann

WHAT YOU BELIEVE IN

Words and Music by Gary Barlow, Jason Orange,
Howard Donald, Mark Owen, Anders Bagge and Henrik Jansson

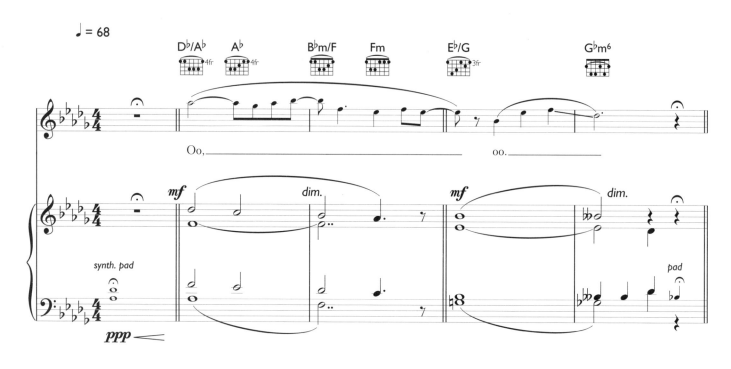

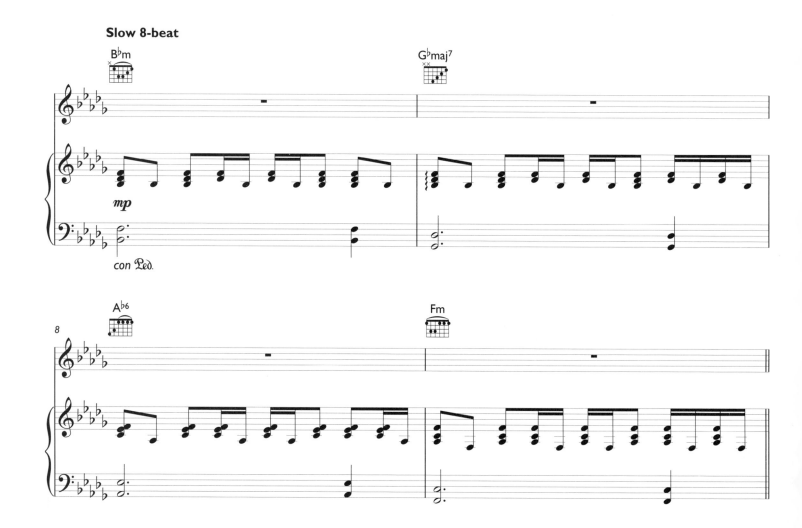

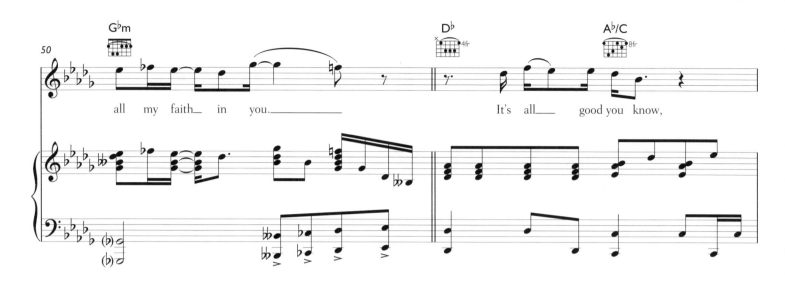

all my faith__ in you._____ It's all__ good you know,

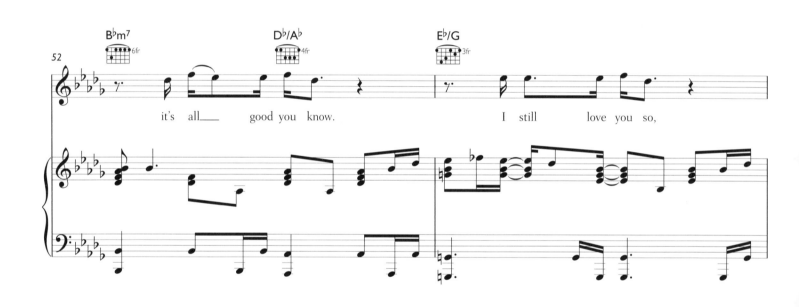

it's all__ good you know. I still love you so,

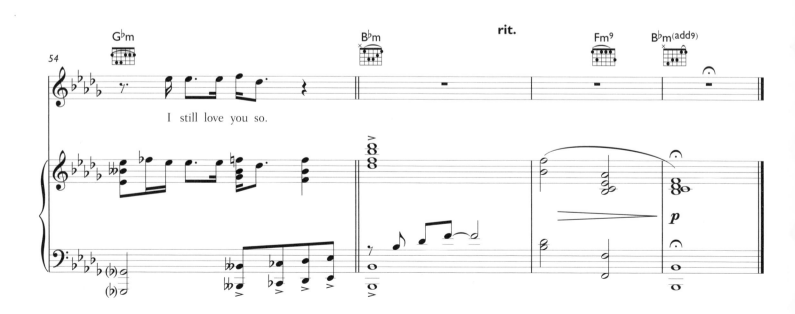

I still love you so.

MANCUNIAN WAY

Words and Music by Gary Barlow, Jason Orange,
Howard Donald, Mark Owen and Eg White

Original key C♯ major

♩ = 76 **Moderate 8-Beat**

1. We used to walk Man - cu - ni - an Way,___ we used to swag-ger, we used___ to sway,___

up un - til the lights took us a - way,___ do you know what you meant___ to me?

We used to think we were___ the bomb, then some-one left a real___ one,___

WOODEN BOAT

Words and Music by Gary Barlow, Jason Orange,
Howard Donald, Mark Owen and Billy Mann

go from green_ to blue_ to gold_ to black;_

breathe deep,_ who knows how long_ this will last.

BUTTERFLY

Words and Music by Gary Barlow, Jason Orange,
Howard Donald, Mark Owen and John Shanks

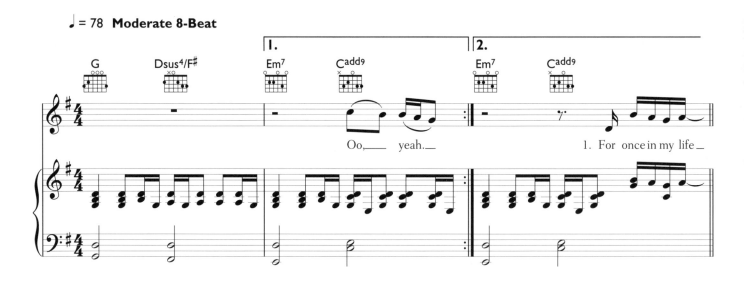

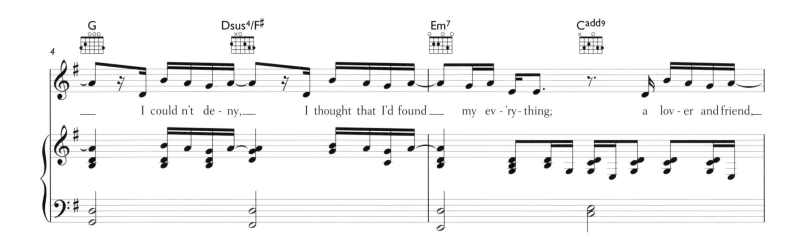

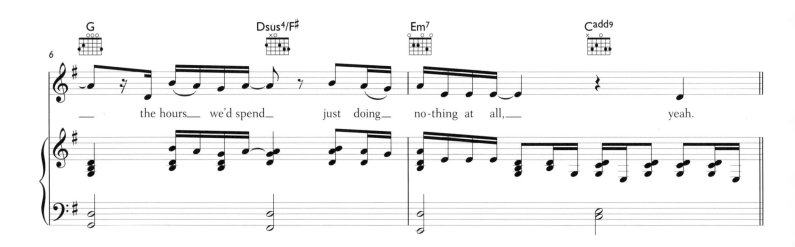

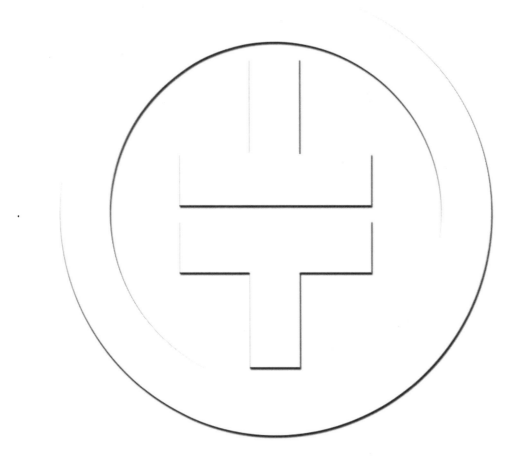